# PRINCIPAL DESIGNER'S HANDBOOK

and Guide to the
**CDM 2015 Regulations**

RIBA ₩ **Publishing**

**Principal Designer's Handbook**

© The Association for Project Safety, 2015

Published by RIBA Publishing, part of RIBA Enterprises Ltd,
The Old Post Office, St Nicholas Street, Newcastle upon Tyne,
NE1 1RH

ISBN 978 1 85946 692 6

Stock code 87202

British Library Cataloguing-in-Publication Data
A catalogue record for this book is available from the
British Library.

Publisher: Steven Cross

Production: Richard Blackburn

Designed and Typeset: Kalina Norton, Studio Kalinka

Illustrations: Pages 6, 12, 13, 33 and 35 - John Banks
Pages 7, 9, 14, 15, and 18 - Andrew Leslie
Page 34 - Grant Bulloch Architect Ltd /
Andrew Leslie

Printed and bound by Page Bros, Norwich, UK

# CONTENTS

## FOREWORD

This Handbook has been prepared to assist organisations and individuals to deliver the new Principal Designer role introduced to the construction industry by the CDM 2015 Regulations on 6 April 2015. It is primarily aimed towards the needs of the single practitioner or small/medium size practices who offer Principal Designer services either as a stand-alone service or in addition to other design services.

The Handbook is intended to assist the industry achieve a proportionate response to Health and Safety Design Risk Management in the Pre-Construction Phase by helping those who have sufficient health and safety skill, knowledge and experience to carry out the Principal Designer role where they feel confident to do so.

The CDM 2015 Regulations have presented the industry with a significant challenge to change the way it delivers design and construction health and safety coordination. The coordination of all project design work and Design Risk Management with respect to health and safety in the Pre-Construction Phase has been placed firmly within the remit of the Principal Designer. CDM 2015 changes the whole dynamic of how and when consideration of design risk commences and concludes.

This authoritative Handbook draws from the skill, knowledge and experience of APS members practising as design risk practitioners to the construction industry for many years, and adds to that the experience gained from the initial period of CDM 2015. The Handbook is easily consulted and provides a quick reference resource for both new Principal Designers and experienced design risk practitioners.

Over and above the practical, day-to-day demands of regulatory compliance and making CDM 2015 work, the industry faces a higher level, strategic challenge to make construction healthier and safer for all involved in or affected by it. CDM 2015 will mean different things to different people. However, we are all in agreement about worker protection and sustainable, safe and healthy design.

Richard G. Wilks, President, The Association for Project Safety

## About The Association for Project Safety

The Association for Project Safety (APS) is the leading membership body for Pre-Construction design and construction health and safety risk management. Its aims are to improve and promote the professional practice of design and construction health and safety risk management. The Association works to set standards and provide guidance, education and training.

## Acknowledgements

**Contributors**
Editorial team: John Banks, Andrew Leslie, John Nielsen and Stella Saunders

**Other contributors**
Gillian Birkby and Graham Leech

# INTRODUCTION

The Principal Designer's Handbook is aimed specifically at Designers taking on the role of Principal Designer on a small/medium sized project, and is intended to help them understand their responsibilities in relation to the CDM Regulations 2015. The Principal Designer controls the Pre-Construction Phase of a construction project, relating to health and safety.

This Handbook will not generally reiterate the content of the Guidance or Regulations (L153) or the Construction Industry Training Board (CITB) guides. It is assumed that readers will have acquired, read and assimilated the contents of these documents.

## Who can be the Principal Designer?

Where there is likely to be more than one Contractor at work on a project at any time, the Client for that project must appoint, in writing, a Principal Designer.

1. The Principal Designer must be:

   o EITHER: one of the design organisations or sole practitioner Designers designing the project.

   o OR: a separate Designer or design organisation not part of the team designing the project

   The CDM 2015 Regulations and Guidance do not specify that the Principal Designer must actually be designing any part of the project.

2. The Principal Designer must be a design organisation or sole practitioner Designer with design experience appropriate to the project.

3. The Principal Designer must have **skills, knowledge and experience** relevant to the design, construction, maintenance and use of the project. A Designer must not accept an appointment for the Principal Designer role unless they have the necessary **skills, knowledge and experience**, and the organisational capability, relevant to the project.

4. The Principal Designer must also have knowledge of and the skill to apply the principles of Design Risk Management, and have knowledge of the CDM 2015 Regulations.

5. Designers offering their services as Principal Designers will need to consider how to establish their organisation's ability and resources to offer the Principal Designer service. Those without previous CDM experience will need to undertake training in order to demonstrate skills and knowledge sufficient to understand and deliver the Principal Designer role.

6. On a commercial project, if a Client fails to appoint a Principal Designer, the obligation to fulfil the Principal Designer duties falls on the Client by default, whether or not they have the necessary **skills, knowledge and experience.**

7. On a domestic project, if a Client fails to appoint a Principal Designer, the Designer in control of the Pre-Construction Phase becomes the Principal Designer by default.

## Role requirements

This Handbook provides the basic support and resources you will need to fulfil the Principal Designer role. You can obtain additional support – including accredited training courses, and access to a website, CDM helpline and legal advice – by becoming a member of The Association for Project Safety (APS). While information has been presented in this Handbook to reflect current good practice, you will also be directed to a designated area on the APS website that will expand on some of the points and will provide the most up-to-date information.

INTRODUCTION

To summarise, the Principal Designer role:

- Is not a replacement for the CDM Coordinator – it is a new role

- Includes duties qualified by the term 'so far as reasonably practicable'

- Is not necessarily complex, particularly on small and straightforward projects; nor does it involve an overly onerous set of tasks for an experienced Designer with suitable health and safety and CDM knowledge and experience

- Is not about an endless round of administration, but rather proactive management and practical, design-based focus on real risk prevention in relation to Pre-Construction health and safety

- Is not a role that practising Designers should shy away from; on more complex projects, Designers may wish to appoint a specialist Health and Safety Consultant with knowledge and experience in Pre-Construction Phase to help them fulfil their duties as Principal Designer.

**What does 'so far as (is) reasonably practicable' mean?**

A suggested definition could be (subject to clarification in a court of law):

*'so far as (is) reasonably practicable' means balancing the level of risk against the measures needed to control the real risk. The Principal Designer (or Designer) is allowed to take considerations such as time, cost, inconvenience and aesthetics into account when determining whether or not it is reasonable and/or practical to redesign part of a project to remove significant risk.*

# 1

# THE
# PRINCIPAL
# DESIGNER ROLE

## 1.1  Role overview

The Principal Designer must plan, manage and monitor the Pre-Construction Phase, and coordinate construction health and safety during this phase to ensure that the project is carried out without risk to health and safety (so far as is reasonably practicable; it is not possible to ensure that construction work is carried out without risk).

### Pre-Construction Phase

**The Pre-Construction Phase is any period during which design or preparatory work is carried out for a project, and often continues during the Construction Phase.**

### Preparation of Pre-Construction Information

The Principal Designer provides assistance to the Client in preparation of Pre-Construction Information, which is continuously developed as follows:

- The Principal Designer will gather and distribute Pre-Construction Information in the Client's possession at the start of the project. In practice, the information a Client has will depend on the type of Client (domestic or commercial), the size and type of project, and so on. Domestic Clients are unlikely to have much information available, but Commercial Clients should have information about their building and site. For example, Commercial Clients instructing refurbishment should have asbestos, structural and services information.

- The Principal Designer and Designers will identify gaps in the Pre-Construction Information where the Client needs to instruct, either themselves or through a consultant, further investigations and studies during the initial design phases.

- The Principal Designer will distribute appropriate Pre-Construction Information to Designers and Contractors.

- The Principal Designer and Designers will identify Pre-Construction Information gaps as the design proceeds.

- The Principal Designer will gather information from the Designers, complete with Design Risk Management information, to pass to the Principal Contractor or tenderers.

- The Principal Designer will continue to gather Pre-Construction Information from Designers (including Contractors undertaking design) during the Construction Phase, and will liaise with the Principal Contractor about how to manage design risks identified during the Pre-Construction Phase.

## Risk management

The Principal Designer must identify, eliminate or control foreseeable risks to health and safety (so far as is reasonably practicable). They are expected to have the necessary skills, knowledge and experience for the size and type of structure(s) on which they are appointed, in order to work with all Designers to identify risk issues to those who construct, use and maintain the structure. This does not mean that all risks must be removed, or all risks listed. Again, remember the definition of 'so far as reasonably practicable'.

## Cooperation of all involved

The Principal Designer must ensure the cooperation of all those involved in a project. They therefore require soft skills and people management capabilities. In many cases a Principal Designer will also be a Designer on the project, and will have both Principal Designer and Designer duties. The Principal Designer has a duty to make sure that the other Designers on the project are also complying with their Designer duties.

The Principal Designer must ensure prompt provision of appropriate Pre-Construction Information to all Designers and all Contractors appointed by the Client. They must pass appropriate Pre-Construction Information to Designers and Contractors at different stages of a project, as and when the information becomes available.

## Extent of the role

The Principal Designer must liaise with the Principal Contractor for the duration of their appointment. An initial Principal Designer may be appointed to provide a partial service (for example, production of drawings and specification only). However, the Client must appoint a Principal Designer for as long as the Pre-Construction Phase lasts. The following scenarios may apply:

- If there is no further design or temporary works design when the Pre-Construction Phase has ended, the Principal Designer role can cease and the Principal Contractor could complete the Health and Safety File.

- If there is continuing design or temporary works design which ceases before the end of the project, a Principal Designer must be appointed (the Client takes on the role by default for commercial projects) while design continues.

- If design or the Principal Designer appointment continues to the end of the project, the Pre-Construction Phase is as long as the Construction Phase, and the Principal Designer appointment needs to continue to mirror the Construction Phase for the Principal Designer to deliver the Health and Safety File to the Client.

- The Principal Designer role may be carried out by the Principal Contractor if they have the capability.

## Health and Safety File

The Principal Designer must prepare an appropriate Health and Safety File during the Pre-Construction Phase. Gathering of information for the File should be a continuous process throughout the Pre-Construction and Construction Phases. The Principal Designer should tailor their approach according to the size and type of project, and is responsible for passing the Health and Safety File to the Client, unless the Principal Designer appointment ends before the conclusion of the project. In these circumstances the Principal Designer must pass the partially completed File to the Principal Contractor for completion and handover to the Client, and advise the Client that this has been done.

## 1.2 Different role responsibilities

The figure below shows who is responsible for carrying out the duties and undertaking the functions within the CDM Regulations 2015. For more about the other duty holders' roles listed here, *see Chapter 5.*

Clients undertaking projects (as part of a business)

| Number of contractors on site at any time | | | |
|---|---|---|---|
| **More than one contractor** | | **Only one contractor** | |
| **Client** | Pre-Construction Information | **Client** | Pre-Construction Information |
| **Designer(s)** | Information with design | **Designer(s)** | Information with design |
| **Principal Designer** (written appointment by Client) | Pre-Construction Information / Health and Safety File | | |
| **Contractor(s)** | Information to workers | **Contractor** | Construction Phase Plan and Information to workers |
| **Principal Contractor** (written appointment by Client) | Construction Phase Plan / Health and Safety File | | |
| **Duty holders** | Providing: | **Duty holders** | Providing: |

Domestic Clients undertaking projects (not as part of a business)

| Number of contractors on site at any time | | | |
|---|---|---|---|
| **More than one contractor** | | **Only one contractor** | |
| **Client** (undertaken by Principal Contractor or Principal Designer if Principal Designer appointed) | Pre-Construction Information | **Client** (undertaken by Contractor) | Pre-Construction Information |
| **Designer(s)** | Information with design | **Designer(s)** | Information with design |
| **Principal Designer** (if appointed) | Pre-Construction Information / Health and Safety File | | |
| **Contractor(s)** | Information to workers | **Contractor** | Construction Phase Plan and Information to workers |
| **Principal Contractor** | Construction Phase Plan / Health and Safety File | | |
| **Duty holders** | Providing: | **Duty holders** | Providing: |

**Figure 1.1**

## 1.3  Commercial projects

The Client, the Principal Designer and the Principal Contractor are the key triumvirate who plan, manage and monitor health and safety in a commercial construction project. Each has a distinct role under CDM 2015 (Chapter 5), and the roles are joined in the common purpose of preventing workers, the public and users coming to any harm. CDM 2015 anticipates that the Principal Designer will be a design organisation, assuming that they have the appropriate skills, knowledge and experience of the type and size of project as Designers, and have the requisite knowledge and understanding of construction health and safety, the relevant legislation and regulation – and CDM 2015 in particular.

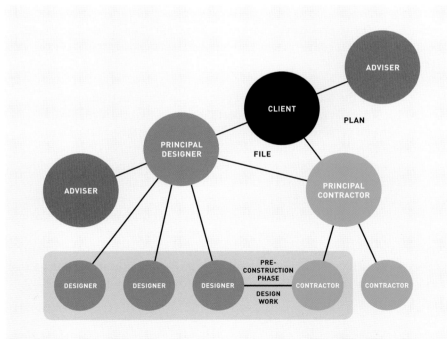

**Figure 1.2**
Key relationships in Pre-Construction Phase design work for commercial projects

If the Lead Designer is capable of undertaking the design work and managing and coordinating the design team, but is not capable of delivering the health and safety services required of a Principal Designer, then two choices are available:

- The Lead Designer can accept the Principal Designer appointment, but subcontract the Principal Designer role to a suitably experienced consultant; in this scenario, the appointed Principal Designer retains the full legal responsibility for the Principal Designer service supplied by their consultant, OR

- The Client can appoint a separate design organisation or individual as Principal Designer.

Designers and Contractors on commercial projects who historically have not had to produce Pre-Construction Information, Construction Phase Plans and Health and Safety Files will require training in order to combine their CDM 2015 roles with their traditional roles.

Figure 1.3 shows the relationships and overlaps in a typical traditionally procured construction project. It is important to note that the Principal Designer role will continue into the Construction Phase for as long as the Pre-Construction Phase continues or as long as the Principal Designer is appointed. This means liaising with the Principal Contractor and Contractors who are carrying out design work. If the Principal Designer appointment concludes at the end of the Pre-Construction Phase, the Principal Designer must hand the Health and Safety File as developed at that date to the Principal Contractor for completion. However, it is better if possible for the Principal Designer role to continue, to avoid the need to pass completion of the Health and Safety File to a different person and to deal with the continuing design that invariably takes place during the Construction Phase on the vast majority of projects.

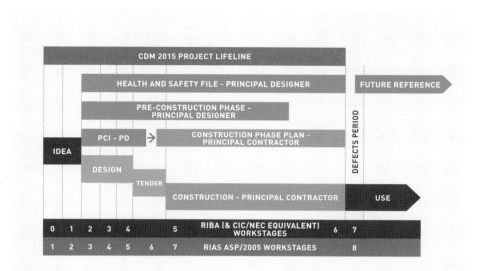

**Figure 1.3**
Overlaps between relationships in a typical traditionally procured construction project

## How the Principal Designer fits into the larger project

In liaison with the Client, Designers and the Principal Contractor, the Principal Designer has an important role in influencing how the risks to health and safety should be managed and incorporated into the wider management of a project.

Decisions about the design taken during the Pre-Construction Phase can have a significant effect on whether the project is delivered in a way that secures health and safety.

The Principal Designer's role involves coordinating the work of others in the project team to ensure that significant and foreseeable risks emanating from construction, use and maintenance are managed throughout the design process.

THE PRINCIPAL DESIGNER ROLE

The Principal Designer should be appointed as early as possible in the design process, if practicable at the concept stage. Appointing the Principal Designer early (RIBA Stage 2 or earlier, or CIC/NEC equivalent – see RIBA Plan of Work 2013) will provide the Client with help in matters such as pulling together the Pre-Construction Information and giving the Principal Designer enough time to carry out their duties. Remember that in commercial projects the Client takes on the role of Principal Designer by default in the absence of a Principal Designer written appointment.

The duration of the Principal Designer's appointment should take into account any design work that may continue into the Construction Phase, or any issues that may arise during construction involving the need to make suitable modifications to the designs.

For projects involving early work by a concept Designer, a Project Management company or where a Design and Build Contractor or novated Designer is subsequently involved, it may be appropriate for the initial Principal Designer appointment to be concluded and a new Principal Designer appointed.

The Principal Designer should be in place for as long as there is a need for their role to be performed.

In conjunction with the Principal Designer, the Client should make sure that the Principal Designer passes the partially completed Health and Safety File to the Principal Contractor so it can be revised during the remainder of the project. *(For more about the Health and Safety File, see page 51.)*

It is not the Principal Designer's responsibility to:

- Submit the notification (F10) to the Health and Safety Executive or check that the Client has done so

- Check the skills and experience of the Designers or Contractors unless they are appointing them directly

- Advise the Client on their appointment of Designers and Contractors, including their skills, knowledge and experience.

- Advise the Client on their health and safety arrangements for the project, including welfare facilities

- Review or approve the Construction Phase Plan or check that it has been implemented

- Appoint the Principal Contractor

- Review or approve health and safety arrangements on site, including method statements

- Take on overall design responsibility for the project – the Principal Designer role is only to manage health and safety during the Pre-Construction Phase

- Supervise or monitor health and safety on site – this is the responsibility of the Principal Contractor

- Check or approve designs; the Principal Designer role involves the review of health and safety risks emanating from the design process.

**Figure 1.4**
The role of the Principal Designer

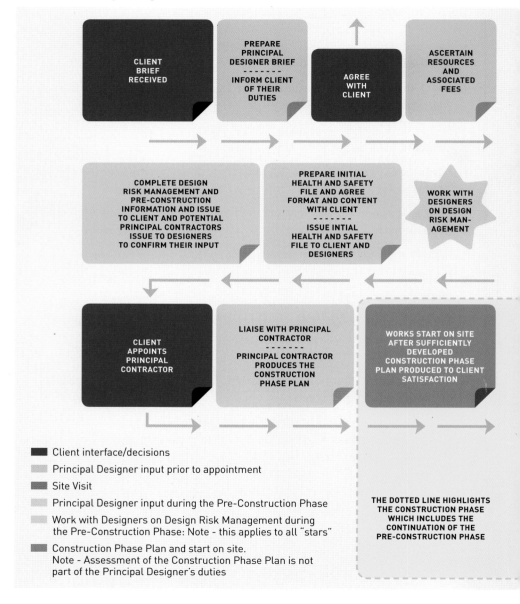

Client interface/decisions

Principal Designer input prior to appointment

Site Visit

Principal Designer input during the Pre-Construction Phase

Work with Designers on Design Risk Management during
the Pre-Construction Phase: Note - this applies to all "stars"

Construction Phase Plan and start on site.
Note - Assessment of the Construction Phase Plan is not
part of the Principal Designer's duties

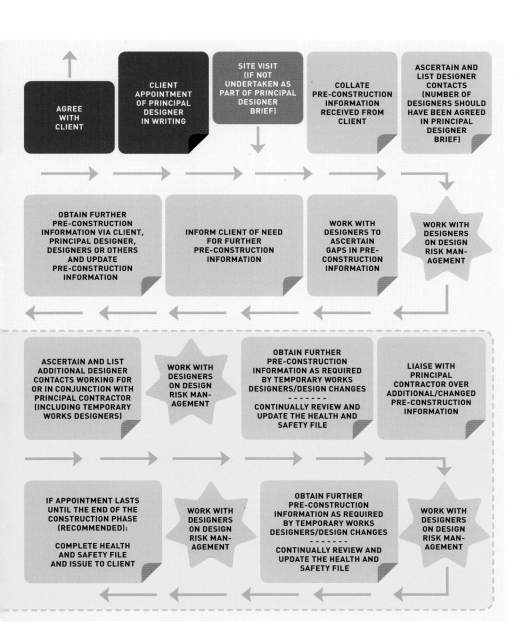

AGREE WITH CLIENT

CLIENT APPOINTMENT OF PRINCIPAL DESIGNER IN WRITING

SITE VISIT (IF NOT UNDERTAKEN AS PART OF PRINCIPAL DESIGNER BRIEF)

COLLATE PRE-CONSTRUCTION INFORMATION RECEIVED FROM CLIENT

ASCERTAIN AND LIST DESIGNER CONTACTS (NUMBER OF DESIGNERS SHOULD HAVE BEEN AGREED IN PRINCIPAL DESIGNER BRIEF)

OBTAIN FURTHER PRE-CONSTRUCTION INFORMATION VIA CLIENT, PRINCIPAL DESIGNER, DESIGNERS OR OTHERS AND UPDATE PRE-CONSTRUCTION INFORMATION

INFORM CLIENT OF NEED FOR FURTHER PRE-CONSTRUCTION INFORMATION

WORK WITH DESIGNERS TO ASCERTAIN GAPS IN PRE-CONSTRUCTION INFORMATION

WORK WITH DESIGNERS ON DESIGN RISK MANAGEMENT

ASCERTAIN AND LIST ADDITIONAL DESIGNER CONTACTS WORKING FOR OR IN CONJUNCTION WITH PRINCIPAL CONTRACTOR (INCLUDING TEMPORARY WORKS DESIGNERS)

WORK WITH DESIGNERS ON DESIGN RISK MANAGEMENT

OBTAIN FURTHER PRE-CONSTRUCTION INFORMATION AS REQUIRED BY TEMPORARY WORKS DESIGNERS/DESIGN CHANGES
- - - - - - -
CONTINUALLY REVIEW AND UPDATE THE HEALTH AND SAFETY FILE

LIAISE WITH PRINCIPAL CONTRACTOR OVER ADDITIONAL/CHANGED PRE-CONSTRUCTION INFORMATION

IF APPOINTMENT LASTS UNTIL THE END OF THE CONSTRUCTION PHASE (RECOMMENDED):

COMPLETE HEALTH AND SAFETY FILE AND ISSUE TO CLIENT

WORK WITH DESIGNERS ON DESIGN RISK MANAGEMENT

OBTAIN FURTHER PRE-CONSTRUCTION INFORMATION AS REQUIRED BY TEMPORARY WORKS DESIGNERS/DESIGN CHANGES
- - - - - - -
CONTINUALLY REVIEW AND UPDATE THE HEALTH AND SAFETY FILE

WORK WITH DESIGNERS ON DESIGN RISK MANAGEMENT

13

## 1.4 Domestic projects

Domestic projects are dealt with slightly differently from commercial projects; the Domestic Client has only one duty – to appoint a Principal Designer and a Principal Contractor. However, if these appointments are not made by the Client, the Designer in control of the Pre-Construction Phase and the Contractor in control of the Construction Phase take on the role of Principal Designer/Principal Contractor by default. All other Client duties are passed to the Principal Contractor, or to the Principal Designer if appointed in writing.

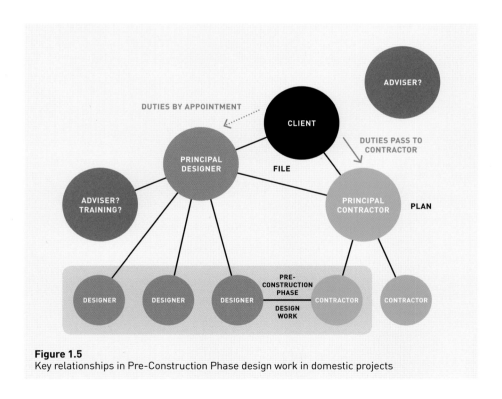

**Figure 1.5**
Key relationships in Pre-Construction Phase design work in domestic projects

Designers and Contractors who historically have not had to notify projects, produce Pre-Construction Information, Construction Phase Plans and Health and Safety Files will require training in order to combine their CDM 2015 roles with their traditional roles, whether or not they decide, initially, to appoint a Sub-consultant to advise them.

On a typical domestic project, the Lead Designer will be the Principal Designer by written appointment or default, and is likely to be in overall control of the management of the project, including acting as Contract Administrator.

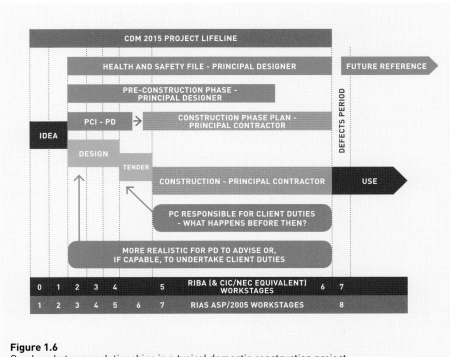

**Figure 1.6**
Overlaps between relationships in a typical domestic construction project

## The Client's role in domestic self-build projects

On domestic projects for self-build Clients the arrangements can be relatively complex. Where the Client controls how construction work is carried out, that Client must comply with Part 4 of CDM 2015 – general requirements for all construction sites. In effect, that Client could be considered to be carrying out the role of the Principal Contractor. Where the self-build Client is also 'designing' and employing Designers for specific roles – e.g. obtaining planning consent and regulation approval – the Client cannot assume the role of Principal Designer unless they are also in business as a Designer. Designers who have a limited involvement in the project may become Principal Designer by default for the period of their appointment.

The Client's lack of health and safety knowledge and experience should be compensated for by the professional Designers providing suitable advice and guidance during their appointment and by Contractors for the duration of their involvement.

## 1.5 Partial design service

On some projects the Designer may be asked to produce design and construction information but their appointments will be terminated before procurement of a Contractor, which the Client will take control of.

Small, simple projects should only require the production of short and simple Pre-Construction Information, evaluation of significant design risk issues, and a short and simple Construction Phase Plan and Health and Safety File.

### Partial design service for domestic projects

On a typical domestic project, the Client will often appoint Designers to undertake the design work, well in advance of the appointment of a Principal Contractor. It therefore makes sense for the Principal Designer to take on the Client's duties at least until a Principal Contractor is appointed. However, the Principal Designer should check liability issues with their professional indemnity insurer first. Taking on the Client's duties will mean that the Principal Designer takes on the responsibility for providing the Pre-Construction Information and setting out the Client's arrangements for managing health and safety for the project, and ensuring that these arrangements are described in the tender documentation. The Principal Designer undertaking the Client duties must also ensure, prior to commencement of construction works, that the Principal Contractor produces a sufficiently developed Construction Phase Plan and that suitable welfare facilities are being provided. During the Construction Phase, which may overlap with the Pre-Construction Phase, the Principal Designer undertaking the Client role will also liaise with the Principal Contractor about how the Principal Contractor will maintain the management arrangements during the Construction Phase.

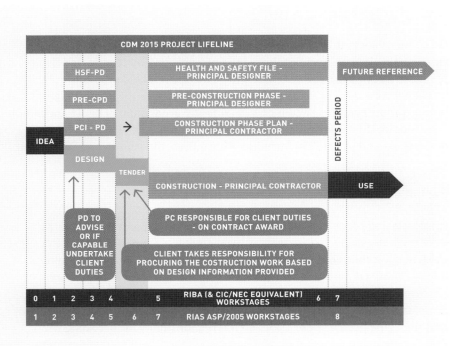

**Figure 1.7**
Overlaps between relationships in a typical domestic construction project with partial design service

For the Domestic Client, the blue area in the diagram represents construction procurement and is a period when neither design nor construction is taking place. This is also a period where there may be a considerable delay between completion of design work and commencement of construction.

In Figure 1.7, the initial Principal Designer appointment has ceased at an agreed point – usually at Building Regulations or tender stage. The Client then takes over the management of the project for the purpose of obtaining prices. This is also a period where there may be a considerable delay between completion of design work and commencement of construction. Once a Principal Contractor is appointed, the Client duties will be transferred to the Principal Contractor or to another Principal Designer (if appointed).

## Information to give to the Client

At the end of their appointment, the Principal Designer needs to hand over information for the Client's use to enable the Client to obtain tender prices and continue with the project. This information should include:

- The drawings and specifications

- The Pre-Construction Information

- The Health and Safety File as developed to that date

- A statement that the Principal Designer role for the project has concluded

- Advice about how to proceed with procurement of a Principal Contractor; the Principal Designer should ensure that the Client is made aware that the Principal Contractor needs to demonstrate CDM 2015 capability as well as technical capability and track record.

## Completion of Principal Designer role

On completion of their role, the Principal Designer should send a letter or email to the Client advising them as follows:

- That the Principal Designer's role has finished; another Principal Designer should be appointed, or the Principal Designer duties could be carried out by the Principal Contractor. The tendering Contractors, one of whom will be responsible for any design changes during the construction period, should also be advised

- That the Client should ensure that the tendering Contractors can demonstrate Principal Contractor awareness and capability, including:

  - track record

  - ability to deal with significant risks identified in the Pre-Construction Information

  - provision of references from other Clients/Advisers.

### Client's responsibility

The Client should then issue the following to the tendering Contractors:

- The Designers' drawings and specifications

- The Pre-Construction Information (if separate)

- The partially developed Health and Safety File.

### Large domestic projects

It is important to note that not all domestic projects are small and simple. Designers should only take on the Principal Designer role if they have the capability to do so or have someone capable to help them discharge their duties. Larger or more complex projects may require the appointment of a Construction Health and Safety (CDM) Adviser to advise and assist the Client and/or Principal Designer.

## Partial design service for commercial projects

The above scenarios can occur on commercial projects, but the Client's duties are not transferred, and the Client takes on the Principal Designer role if they do not appoint a Principal Designer in writing.

**2**

# THE PRINCIPAL DESIGNER IN PRACTICE

## 2.1  Appointment and fees

The Principal Designer role should not be considered an insignificant 'bolt-on' to a design service, and remuneration should be considered separately. Even for the simplest project, the role of Principal Designer will require resources beyond those required to undertake technical and CDM Designer duties.

### Extent of the Principal Designer's function and duties

Initial discussions about the role and scope of the Client's duties, the role and duties of the Principal Designer, and any possible additional services that the Client may require should be used to establish the service agreement. It is worth sending a letter/email outlining the basic Principal Designer duties to provide a framework for these discussions.

It is a good idea to use a standard APS Form of Appointment as Principal Designer, as a starting point for discussions. This can be followed up by an appropriately completed Form of Appointment, with a covering letter.

A schedule of services should be agreed. For an industry-standard approach, refer to Schedule 1 (Schedule of Services) of the APS Form of Appointment as Principal Designer.

http://www.aps.org.uk/publications

### Separate roles

It is important when acting as both Lead Designer and Principal Designer to identify the services being provided for the Principal Designer role, and the period in the project programme during which these services are required. This may differ from the Lead Designer arrangements. It is not sensible to simply state 'provide Principal Designer services as per CDM 2015' as an addendum or insert to a Form of Appointment for technical design services. Separate forms of appointment or bespoke appointment letters should be used which clearly set out the services being provided and the fees being charged for these services. Use of the APS Terms of Appointment is recommended.

## Determining a fee

To determine the fee for your role as Principal Designer you should establish the resources and time it will take to fulfil the role, bearing in mind what you have to legally provide to the Client over and above the requirements for a Designer. CDM 2015 requires by law sufficient resources to be provided to enable the Principal Designer to fulfil their duties, and you will need to demonstrate this to the Client. When estimating costs and expenses, you should include:

- Staff time

- Additional resources required, including specialists

- Overheads

- Travel for site visits and attendance at design/project team meetings

- Assisting the Client in providing the Pre-Construction Information and the delivery of documents, such as drawings, reports, any Designer deliverables and the Health and Safety File(s).

THE PRINCIPAL DESIGNER IN PRACTICE

It is good practice for fees to be based on an assessment of work hours required, overlaid on the current project programme, incidental costs and estimated overheads for the Principal Designer work on the project.

## Resources for Domestic projects

When working for Domestic Clients, Designers who are in control of the Pre-Construction Phase (usually the Architect) may find themselves being asked to undertake the Principal Designer role by the Client. Bear in mind that if the Client does not appoint the Designer as Principal Designer, then that Designer may well find that they are taking on the role by default, only without any agreed fee for doing so.

Designers on domestic projects are advised to provide their Client with a fee for both the design services and for undertaking the Principal Designer duties with their initial fee proposal if they wish to ensure that they have sufficient resources allocated to discharge their roles. It is advisable for the Designer to make a record within their fees of the resource allocated to each service they are providing, in order to be able to demonstrate that they have made adequate provision.

The APS resource estimator is available to members at
http://aps.legallio.com/aps-principal-designer-adviser-resource-estimator/183/11/16/3

### Site visit

The Principal Designer should visit the site to assess the health and safety issues affecting the project, preferably before the fee agreement is concluded. If this is not possible, the use of Google Street View is useful but should always be supplemented by an actual site visit.

## Keeping project changes under review

Changes in service provision can come about for a number of reasons, including demands made as a result of the unsuitable or unsatisfactory performance of others; significant changes in the nature, timing or scope of the project; and termination of any of the project appointments. It is therefore important to:

- Constantly reassess the Principal Designer role

- Be proactive in any dialogue with the Client

- Seek changes to the terms of the Principal Designer appointment where significant changes to the project occur, or where significant under-compliance by any party increases the Principal Designer workload

- Inform other appointees of any changes to your instructions.

## Novation – design and build contracts

In the early stages of a design and build project, before the Design and Build Contractor is appointed, there is almost always some design work carried out. The Client should appoint a Principal Designer for this early design work.

If the Designer appointed as Principal Designer has been novated to the Design and Build Contractor and can no longer fulfil the Principal Designer role, the Client must appoint a new Principal Designer. One obvious choice for the role will be the Design and Build Contractor. Even if they have no Designers working for them in-house, the Design and Build Contractor could fulfil the role as Principal Designer by making arrangements with one of the novated Designers to carry out those functions. There is no problem with this under the Regulations. If the same Designer acts as Principal Designer throughout, this has the added advantage of providing continuity.

## Late appointment

In the case of late appointment, the Principal Designer will need to inform the Client of any significant health and safety implications, which can include:

- Time required to enable Pre-Construction Information to be obtained and provided to Designers

- Time for checks that management arrangements are in place to enable satisfactory planning; managing and monitoring of the Pre-Construction Phase, and the coordination of all relevant matters

- Time required to enable the Principal Designer to revisit design work to check suitability and compatibility of designs

- Time for cooperation with the Principal Contractor to ensure they have all the relevant information they need to proceed

- Missed opportunities to eliminate, reduce and manage risk and reduce whole-life costs

- Failure to take into account the General Principles of Prevention. (The General Principles of Prevention are described in Chapter 2.4)

It is important to identify the areas where the late-appointed Principal Designer cannot fully discharge their duties and for which the Client is responsible; the Principal Designer role defaults to the Client with non-appointment.

### Additional CDM 2015 services

In many instances, the Principal Designer will be asked to provide additional CDM 2015 services (see Chapter 5.9 - the CDM Adviser) but should carefully consider their capability to undertake these.

### Exemplar letters

Some typical wordings for letters from the Principal Designer to the Client are included in Chapter 4.

## 2.2  Pre-Construction Information

### Client's responsibilities

A Client must provide Pre-Construction Information as soon as is practicable to every Designer and Contractor appointed, or being considered for appointment, to the project. Pre-Construction Information is information that is already in the Client's possession (such as an existing Health and Safety File, an asbestos survey, structural drawings, services, etc.), or which is straightforward to obtain through reasonable enquiry. The Client should expect the Principal Designer to help bring the Pre-Construction Information together and provide it to the Designers and Contractors involved.

Appendix 2 of L153 gives further guidance on the provision of Pre-Construction Information, which must include proportionate information about:

- The project, such as the Client brief and key dates of the Construction Phase

- The planning and management of the project, such as the resources and time being allocated to each stage of the project and the arrangements to ensure that there is cooperation between duty holders and that the work is coordinated. It is a Client duty to supply this information. It is not a Principal Designer duty to assist the Client with these arrangements. ✳

- The health and safety hazards of the site, including design and construction hazards and how they will be addressed

- Any relevant information in an existing Health and Safety File.

The information should be in a convenient form and must be clear, concise and easily understandable to help other duty holders involved in the project to carry out their duties. The Principal Designer will assist the Client to assemble information, identify gaps and make reasonable enquiries about obtaining information about their premises (building and land) and local environment.

✳ THE PD MUST HELP THE CLIENT TO TAKE REASONABLE STEPS TO OBTAIN THE INFORMATION

## Typical Client information

- Client brief and requirements

- Key dates during the Construction Phase

- Geotechnical and contaminated land surveys

- Existing services locations (private and public)

- Structural/building safety reports

- Survey reports for hazardous materials (e.g. lead, asbestos)

- Survey reports for hazardous areas (e.g. confined spaces)

- Survey reports for hazardous locations (e.g. fragile roof access)

- Site access and other restrictions

- Local environmental conditions and adjacent land uses

- Neighbours (e.g. schools, petrol stations, supermarkets and major roadways)

- The current Health and Safety File

- For occupied sites, proposed site rules (e.g. existing permit to work systems)

- Proximity of watercourses, transport systems and so on

- Any history of previous damage (e.g. from fire or floods)

## Principal Designer's responsibilities

The Pre-Construction Information is initially prepared or made available by the Client (with the assistance of the Principal Designer) for distribution to the Designers. Depending on the nature of the project, the Designers will then add to, and seek further information for, the Pre-Construction Information, as the design process progresses and becomes more detailed.

The Pre-Construction Information (continuously developed by the Principal Designer during the initial design) is intended to be passed to the Designers. It will:

- Provide information about the project

- Provide information about risks identified during the design process. This can be in the form of a Project Risk Register.

- Provide details of the type of work and activities that the Client foresees or intends to undertake

- Provide details of any ongoing use or occupation of parts of the site or areas adjoining the site so the Designers can take this into account when considering space, access and methods of work

- Alert the Designers to health and safety hazards associated with the site or its surroundings or use while the Construction Phase is under way

- Provide details of the arrangements already in place and/or expected by the Client for the planning and the management of the project

- Provide health and safety information about any existing structures or parts of structures, through the provision of any relevant existing Health and Safety File(s)

- Create a 'level playing field' for pricing (so that those offering to carry out design work will be less likely to put in a low price because of omissions of health and safety management).

## Pre-Construction considerations

Most project design work is 'preparing for construction', with decisions being made that affect health and safety. The following may affect the Pre-Construction Information:

- Client needs, design brief, scope, and costs

- Land acquisition and ownership

- Establishing the needs and liaising with stakeholders and neighbouring 'enterprises'

- Activities in multiple occupied areas

- Assessing the availability of personnel, materials, supplies and other resources

- Undertaking site surveys comprising topographic, geotechnical (strength and stability) and geoenvironmental (chemical and contamination). Note that all ground investigations should be preceded by a desk-top study

- Structural investigation

- Services (public and private)

- Asbestos, lead and other specialist surveys

- Construction feasibility, or constructability, reviews

- Estimating time and sequences of works

- Design decisions

- Temporary works

- Project/site logistics plan.

These factors are often overlooked in Design and Construction Risk Management, and the effects that decisions made in these areas may have on the risks to health or safety of the project are often misunderstood or underestimated, resulting in unexpected additional costs and delay to the Client during construction.

Take account of the nature, scale and complexity of the health or safety matters involved in the project and activities required for the whole life of the project when establishing suitable arrangements as Principal Designer for, and throughout, the Pre-Construction Phase.

## 2.3 Pre-Construction Information development

### Designers

When developing Pre-Construction Information, the Principal Designer should meet the Designers and discuss any issues that arise. They must ensure that Design Risk Management issues are discussed in design review meetings, team meetings, health and safety coordination meetings and workshops for specific issues and continuing communication.

Supplementary Pre-Construction Information provided by Designers as the design of the project progresses should:

- Be relevant

- Have an appropriate level of detail

- Be proportionate to the risks involved.

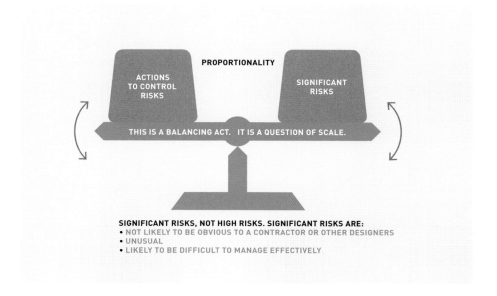

PROPORTIONALITY

ACTIONS TO CONTROL RISKS

SIGNIFICANT RISKS

THIS IS A BALANCING ACT. IT IS A QUESTION OF SCALE.

SIGNIFICANT RISKS, NOT HIGH RISKS. SIGNIFICANT RISKS ARE:
- NOT LIKELY TO BE OBVIOUS TO A CONTRACTOR OR OTHER DESIGNERS
- UNUSUAL
- LIKELY TO BE DIFFICULT TO MANAGE EFFECTIVELY

Pre-Construction Information gathered during the Pre-Construction Phase should be incorporated into drawings, where possible. In addition to drawings, a document should be prepared, if required, to describe emergency procedures, the surrounding environment and the Client's management arrangements during construction. Significant risk information should be highlighted on drawings with symbols and a brief description.

**Remember, the Pre-Construction Phase extends for as long as design is taking place.**

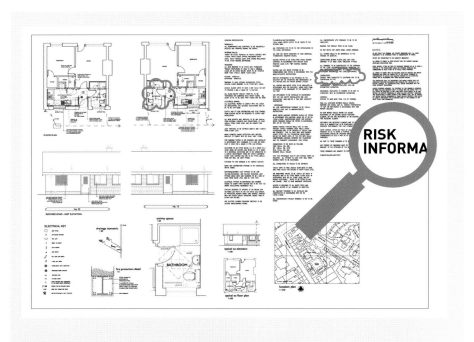

**Figure 2.1**
When passing Pre-Construction Information to Contractors who may be tendering for the work, written information is almost always required, even on smaller projects - but information on drawings may be all that is required on simple projects

## Principal Designer

The Principal Designer should use a schedule to keep a record of required information as it is received. This should cover:

- Adequacy of information provided
- Date of receipt and source of information.

### Significant remaining risk information from Designers

When receiving information on significant remaining risk from Designers, check the following:

- Is the information clear, precise and in a form suitable for others?
- Could or should the information be on a drawing?

The Principal Designer should log the responses from Designers; it is easy to lose track of returns. The Principal Designer should be proactive about seeking information.

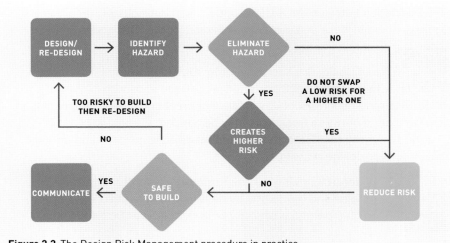

**Figure 2.2** The Design Risk Management procedure in practice

## Contractor's Designers

A Principal Designer should be involved in considering the health and safety implications of all design work on a project, including design undertaken during the Construction Phase, which also covers temporary works.

Considerations when liaising with Designers during the Construction Phase include the following:

- The Principal Contractor should let the Principal Designer know which design will be used and how they are proposing to plan, manage, monitor and coordinate these packages.

- The Principal Contractor should keep a project directory up-to-date so that it is clear who is responsible for which design packages.

- A programme showing proposed dates and the duration of the appointments of these designs is essential for the Client (and the Principal Designer) to determine whether the arrangements are likely to be adequate to enable the Designers to discharge their duties.

- Invite the Principal Contractor to design team meetings to support coordination between the designs undertaken during the Pre-Construction Phase and those undertaken by other Designers during the Construction Phase.

- The Principal Designer should use progress meetings and continuing liaison with the Principal Contractor (as advised in paragraph 104 of L153) to remain abreast of design development and identify where closer coordination between Designers may be needed. Even if they cannot attend all these meetings, they should receive the minutes and periodic coordinated design drawings.

- There is an overarching duty for the Principal Contractor and Principal Designer to liaise and cooperate, so be prepared for conversations and meetings throughout the process to help resolve specific issues.

## 2.4 General Principles of Prevention

The General Principles of Prevention (from the Management of Health and Safety at Work Regulations 1999) provide the framework to help the Principal Designer identify and implement measures to control risks on a construction project.

The following information is taken from HSE's L153 'Managing health and safety in construction', Appendix 1 part 2.

The general principles of prevention are to:

- Avoid risks

- Evaluate the risks which cannot be avoided

- Combat the risks at source

- Adapt the work to the individual, especially regarding the design of workplaces, the choice of work equipment and the choice of working and production methods, with a view, in particular, to alleviating monotonous work, work at a predetermined work rate and to reducing their effect on health

- Adapt to technical progress

- Replace the dangerous by the non-dangerous or the less dangerous

- Develop a coherent overall prevention policy which covers technology, organisation of work, working conditions, social relationships and the influence of factors relating to the working environment

- Give collective protective measures priority over individual protective measures

- Give appropriate instructions to employees.

THE PRINCIPAL DESIGNER IN PRACTICE

In general terms, hazard identification and risk assessment are processes by which Designers and the Principal Designer will interrogate the design work as it progresses.

### ERIC

Once the Principal Designer has evaluated the risk, they must consider how to control it. Think 'ERIC': Eliminate, Reduce, Inform, Control of significant risks resulting from building/use/maintenance by the Contractor/Principal Contractor/Structure Users.

The Principal Designer and other Designers must have the skills, knowledge and experience to identify the risks associated with the:

- Site conditions

- Site surroundings

- Structure – erecting, installing or constructing the structures and elements they are designing

- Materials used in their design

- Work activities necessary to make their design a reality

- Maintenance and cleaning of the structure for its whole life

- Replacement of the parts or elements forming the design

- Impact and effect the carrying out of any of the above work may have on the people affected by the construction

- Use of the structure as a place of work.

## 2.5  Particular Risks

A Construction Phase Plan prepared by the Principal Contractor must include specific measures to address any risk information provided by the Client or Principal Designer in relation to the Particular Risks identified in the HSE's L153, 'Managing health and safety in construction', and listed below. Whilst not stated in L153, the Principal Designer should identify Particular Risks, and include these in the Pre-Construction Information. The Principal Designer should review the responses to the Particular Risks with the Principal Contractor, as these may have an impact on buildability, use and maintenance.

The following information is taken from HSE's L153 'Managing health and safety in construction', Schedule 3 – Particular Risks:

1. Work which puts workers at risk of burial under earthfalls, engulfment in swampland or falling from a height, where the risk is particularly aggravated by the nature of the work or processes used or by the environment at the place of work or site.

2. Work which puts workers at risk from chemical or biological substances constituting a particular danger to the safety or health of workers or involving a legal requirement for health monitoring.

3. Work with ionising radiation requiring the designation of controlled or supervised areas under regulation 16 of the Ionising Radiations Regulations 1999.

4. Work near high voltage power lines.

5. Work exposing workers to the risk of drowning.

6. Work on wells, underground earthworks and tunnels.

7. Work carried out by divers having a system of air supply.

8. Work carried out by workers in caissons with a compressed air atmosphere.

9. Work involving the use of explosives.

10. Work involving the assembly or dismantling of heavy prefabricated components.

Some of these Particular Risks will not occur on many projects, particularly small and domestic projects.

In order to identify where any of the above Particular Risks might be an issue, the Principal Designer should review the nature of the works and activities on the project, the surroundings, ground conditions and adjoining sites. Always ensure that information about these works is known to, and shared by, the Designers and others in the Pre-Construction Phase. Information about any residual works and risks (after the Designers have sought to eliminate the risks through the subsequent design process) should be provided to Contractors and the Principal Contractor in good time to allow for the information to be taken into account in allocating resources, including time and money. This information will form part of the Pre-Construction Information.

Design Risk Management is the term given to the management process in the Pre-Construction Phase that seeks to deliver a design that meets all the health and safety requirements, and that makes building, using, maintaining and demolishing the project safe for workers and users.

The next section describes the principles of Design Risk Management.

## 2.6  Design Risk Management

A common misconception among Designers since the introduction of the CDM Regulations has been to think that the Design Risk Management process required them simply to identify the residual hazards in their designs and to provide information so that others (usually the Contractor) could deal with the risk issues. In fact, it is essential that Designers direct their actions towards eliminating hazards and, if they cannot do this, towards reducing risks through design decisions or provisions. Only as a last resort should Designers rely on actions by the Contractors on site to provide the means of protection for workers and others during work activities. (Remember ERIC *– see page 38.)*

## Design considerations that will inform Design Risk Management

- What is being built? What should it look like, and what is its function?

- Where is the project being built?

- What materials will be used, and how will they be specified?

- How will it be built (risks to site workers, users and/or the general public)?

- When will it be built, how long will it take to build (or how long does the Client want to allow)?

- What are the constraints and circumstances affecting the design and construction?

- Who else is designing this, and what elements or aspects are they addressing?

- What is happening on the adjacent sites or areas?

- What will be continuing to be done or used on the site during the Construction Phase?

- Is this a structure that will be used as a workplace and/or used by the general public?

- How will this structure or element be maintained (risks to site workers, maintainers, users and/or the general public)?

- How will this structure be cleaned, accessed, altered, refurbished, removed or demolished?

**Designers must (so far as is reasonably practicable):**

- Identify forseeable hazards, and particular and significant risks affecting health and safety

- Eliminate hazards

- Minimise remaining identified risks by design

- Consider pre-fabrication to minimise hazardous work (e.g. pre-fabricated and pre-stressed concrete bridge beams)

- Design in features to reduce risks, (i.e. from working at height, deep excavations, etc.)

- Ensure that designs are suitable and compatible with any interacting or interrelating designs

- Take into account the Workplace (Health, Safety and Welfare) Regulations 1992 (and Amendments)

- Provide information on significant risks associated with their design (e.g. information on drawings, suggested construction sequences)

- Identify any future cleaning, maintenance, alteration and demolition hazards for the Health and Safety File.

**Design Risk Management procedures must address the following:**

- Identification, elimination and reduction of hazards and risks

- Proportional responses to foreseeable hazards and risks

- Adequate time allowances for design and construction programming (the right information to the right people at the right time)

- Undertaking systematic design reviews at suitable stages to check for significant risks and issues and coordinated management responses – see RIBA Plan of Work and the Construction Industry Council (CIC) Scope of Services, Stages 2, 3 and 4

- Ensuring effective cooperation with adjacent sites

- Keeping adequate records of the Design Risk Management process – not everything; everything that is significant

- Reviewing hazard and risk information before design information is issued

- Providing hazard and risk information in a clear, concise and appropriate format.

## Information sharing – practical advice

It is the Principal Designer's duty to ensure, so far as is reasonably practicable, that information is being passed on to those who need it, when they need it – even though they may not know they need it – including what is needed by the Client, other Designers, those tendering, Principal Contractor and, if necessary, other Contractors.

On any project, the application of Design Risk Management requires a few basic steps and documents. The effort given to the following needs to be appropriate and proportionate to the nature of the design and to the nature and complexity of the health and safety issues:

- Identify ownership of risk/hazard issues to ensure actions are taken

- Ensure all Designers are included in the process

- Try to close out risk/hazard issues before information is finalised and passed on to those who need it.

**Design Risk Management checklist**

Design Risk Management should take place during:

- Feasibility – Preparation and Brief (RIBA Stage 1 or CIC/NEC equivalent)

- Outline design – Concept Design (RIBA Stage 2 or CIC/NEC equivalent)

- Detailed design stages – Developed Design and Technical Design (RIBA Stages 3 and 4 or CIC/NEC equivalents)

- Construction – (RIBA Stage 5 or CIC/NEC equivalent)

The Principal Designer should ensure that Designers contribute to the agreed project Design Risk Management method (using a consistent pro-forma). They must talk, communicate by other means and keep all appropriate parties in the loop. They must also provide information about their design for construction and the Health and Safety File.

Designers should critically assess their design proposals at an early stage, and then throughout the design process, to ensure that health and safety issues are identified, integrated into the overall design process and addressed as they go along. It is pointless to complete the design first, and to then try to address the risks that the design has introduced. By then, all of the key decisions are likely to have been taken and no one will be willing to make any changes because of the time and cost involved.

## Evaluating the Design Risk Management procedure

**Principal Designers are responsible for ensuring the Design Risk Management process is being undertaken by Designers and for collating the results**

- Is there any evidence of Design Risk Management by the Designers?

- Is there a need to query any Design Risk Management conclusions?

- Does the information relate to significant hazards or risks and unusual or difficult-to-manage elements of construction? Information about risks that a capable and experienced Contractor should be aware of need not be included.

- When hazards are identified but no action is recorded by Designers:

  - explain the implications of the lack of records should an investigation be made later

  - explain the implications should changes to the design be required in order to build the structure due to lack of information

  - request that Designers provide records of their Design Risk Management procedures and actions on hazard elimination and risk reduction.

## Eliminating and managing risk

Below are examples of high and significant risks that Designers are likely to be able to eliminate or manage through good design.

**Risks to health include:**

- Disturbance of asbestos insulation board
- Manual lifting of cladding/glazing panels
- Application of solvent-based floor adhesive in a windowless room
- Welding in confined spaces
- Noise, dust and vibration from concrete scabbling
- Maintenance of plant in a confined space.

**Risks to safety include:**

- Buried, concealed or overhead services
- A major project in an operational educational establishment
- Hot work during a refurbishment project
- Poor site layout for safe vehicle and pedestrian movement
- Unintentional collapse during temporary works or demolition
- Civil engineering work on a live motorway.

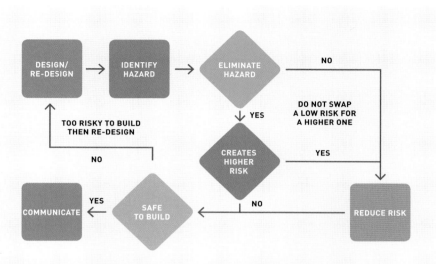

**Figure 2.3**
The Design Risk Management procedure in practice

## Significant risk

Bear in mind that there is a difference between high risk and significant risk. Significant risks are those that are:

- Not likely to be obvious to a Contractor or other Designers

- Unusual

- Likely to be difficult to manage effectively.

## Summary

Designers do not have to eliminate all risks, but if they let them remain they do need to justify this. They must identify foreseeable significant residual risks and communicate these clearly to others. The Principal Designer should ask questions and prompt the Designers to comply with good Design Risk Management and the intentions of CDM 2015.

## 2.7 Preparing the Health and Safety File

The Health and Safety File is intended to highlight significant health and safety risks for future construction work, and is required for projects involving more than one Contractor. It is important to note that it is not a maintenance and operation manual.

The Principal Designer must prepare the Health and Safety File, and review, update and revise it as the project progresses. The Principal Designer must also pass the completed Health and Safety File to the Client to keep.

If the Principal Designer's appointment finishes before the end of the project, the Health and Safety File must be passed to the Principal Contractor for the remainder of the project. The Principal Contractor must then take responsibility for reviewing, updating and revising it and passing it to the Client when the project finishes.

## Content of the Health and Safety File

The Health and Safety File should contain the following:

- A brief description of the work carried out
- Details of any hazards that have not been eliminated through the design and construction processes, and how they have been addressed
- Key structural principles and safe working loads for floors and roofs
- Hazardous materials used (e.g. lead paints and special coatings)
- Information regarding the removal or dismantling of installed plant and equipment
- Health and safety information about equipment provided for cleaning or maintaining the structure
- The nature, location and markings of significant services
- Information and as-built drawings of the building, and its plant and equipment (e.g. the means of safe access for window cleaning; fire strategy drawings).

## Pointers for preparation of the Health and Safety File

There should be enough detail in the Health and Safety File to allow the likely risks to be identified and addressed by those carrying out work in the future. The level of detail should be proportionate to the risks. Information must be in a convenient form, clear, concise and easily understandable.

The Health and Safety File is an information resource that is needed by the Client to inform them of any residual health and safety issues and for them to hand to any Designer/Principal Designer or Contractor/Principal Contractor involved in a new construction project on the existing structure/building. The information in the Health and Safety File will, for example, allow the Client to develop fire risk assessments and to be able to develop risk assessments for the maintenance of structures, and to meet any requirements of specific warranties attached to material/equipment.

The Principal Designer, when handing the Health and Safety File to the Client at the end of the project, should advise the Client of its purpose and importance. The Client should be advised that any relevant information from a future project should be added to the Health and Safety File. This would usually be provided by a Principal Designer or Principal Contractor, but it should be noted that information to update the File could come from a one-contractor piece of work, where the Regulations do not require a Health and Safety File to be prepared.

The Health and Safety File does not need to include information that will be of no help when planning future work, such as:

- Pre-Construction Information that has no health and safety relevance to future work on the structure(s)

- The Construction Phase Plans of any previous projects

- Information generated during the Construction Phase, such as risk assessments, written systems of work and (Construction Phase) COSHH assessments

- Details about the normal operation of the completed structure or its parts or elements

- Construction Phase accident statistics

- Details of all the Contractors, Suppliers, Manufacturers and Designers involved in this and previous projects

- Contractual documents

- Information about structures, or parts of structures, that have been demolished – unless there are any implications for remaining or future structures or works.

Information contained in other documents can be cross-referenced in the file to avoid duplication of information.

# 3

# LIAISON WITH THE PRINCIPAL CONTRACTOR

## 3.1 The Construction Phase

### Tender/pricing stage

In any project the Pre-Construction Information provided by the Client and Designers, and reviewed and managed by the Principal Designer, should form part of the package of information passed to the Contractors with the design information, all for the purposes of tendering for the project. In a traditional project this will occur at the end of RIBA Stage 4 (or CIC/NEC equivalent); in a design and build project this could occur at any stage from RIBA Stage 3 onwards. In all cases the information is passed to the tendering Contractors so that they can take account of the risk information provided and make suitable resource provision for dealing with them. The Pre-Construction Information may be on drawings and in a stand-alone Pre-Construction Information document, or incorporated into the tender documents.

### Contractor acceptance

The Principal Designer provides the Pre-Construction Information to the tendering Contractors. It is common sense – though not a CDM 2015-specific duty – that the Principal Designer should comment on the responses relating to how significant risks will be dealt with to identify any obvious omissions or misinterpretations that may affect the validity of the tender.

### Initial arrangements for liaison

The Principal Designer is responsible for planning, managing and monitoring the Pre-Construction Phase for as long as their appointment lasts, including the parts of the Construction Phase that involve design (Pre-Construction Work). The Principal Designer should, as soon as the Principal Contractor is selected, make arrangements to liaise with the Principal Contractor regarding initial design work by Contractors, including scaffolding, other temporary works, any site preparation (e.g. ground stabilisation or crane bases) and stripping out and demolitions.

## The Construction Phase Plan in practice

The Regulations require the Client to ensure that a Construction Phase Plan is drawn up by the sole Contractor if there is only one, or by the Principal Contractor if there is more than one, before construction work begins. In projects for Domestic Clients, the Domestic Client can appoint the Principal Designer to carry out the Client duties; otherwise the Domestic Client's duties are to be carried out by the sole Contractor or the Principal Contractor. Most Commercial Clients will need assistance with this duty. The Principal Designer has no duty to review the content of the Construction Phase Plan.

There is no requirement in the Regulations for any duty holder to check the sufficiency or suitability of the Construction Phase Plan. However, the Client has an absolute obligation to ensure that the Construction Phase Plan is drawn up, so that it sets out the health and safety arrangements and site rules and takes account of specific risks on the project in question. If a Client is not confident in fulfilling this obligation:

- The Client could employ an CDM Adviser to assist with their duties

- The Client could ask the Principal Designer to undertake a review of the Construction Phase Plan.

The Principal Designer has a duty to liaise with the Principal Contractor for the duration of their appointment, and this includes liaison regarding design development during the Construction Phase, and the coordination of health and safety matters during the Construction Phase.

## 3.2  Continuing liaison during the Construction Phase

Dealing with design changes by Designers and Contractors during the Construction Phase is part of the Principal Designer's role, and the Principal Designer will consider the impact of these design changes on the Design Risk Management strategy for the project in consultation with the Principal Contractor.

The effort the Principal Designer and the Principal Contractor devote to carrying out this liaison should be in proportion to the size and complexity of the project and the nature of risks involved. The Principal Contractor should expect and receive help from the Principal Designer, and any other duty holders on larger projects, in identifying the risks associated with the work and determining the necessary controls that need to be put in place. Regular meetings will usually be the most effective management tool.

While liaising with the Principal Contractor, the Principal Designer's objectives must include:

- Sharing of Pre-Construction Information that may affect the planning, management and monitoring of both the Pre-Construction and the Construction Phases

- Coordination of matters relating to Pre-Construction Health and Safety

- Provision of the Pre-Construction Information needed by the Principal Contractor to review and update the Construction Phase Plan

- Effective management of ongoing design, especially design changes

- Obtaining information for the Health and Safety File.

## Liaison with the Principal Contractor for the Health and Safety File

Unless the Principal Designer's appointment finishes before the end of the Construction Phase, the Principal Designer should continue to liaise with the Principal Contractor regarding information for the Health and Safety File. If the Principal Designer's appointment finishes before the end of the Construction Phase, the Principal Designer should pass the incomplete Health and Safety File developed to that date to the Principal Contractor, and advise the Client that this has taken place. The Principal Contractor should continue to develop the information for the Health and Safety File until the end of the project, when the Health and Safety File is handed to the Client.

The Principal Designer's duty to prepare the Health and Safety File requires the Client, Designers and Principal Contractor to prepare and assemble information and then pass this to the Principal Designer.

The Regulations do not expressly require the Principal Designer to check the accuracy of the information in the Health and Safety File, but everyone providing information should make sure that it is accurate, comprehensible and provided at the appropriate time. However, the duty on the Principal Designer to 'review, update and revise [the File] from time to time ...' does require a proactive response to existing or missing information.

## 3.3  The defects liability period

### Practical completion/handover

It is quite common for there to be a list of incomplete works when the project is handed over to the Client for occupation. These works are construction works and should be considered to be a part of the project, to be completed as soon as possible by the Principal Contractor. This will require appropriate welfare to be provided along with management of the construction and the risks associated with the new circumstances – i.e. working within an occupied building. This is not a new project, but will require the Client, Principal Designer and Principal Contractor to establish arrangements that reflect the changed circumstances. The Principal Designer should provide new or reworked Pre-Construction Information to the Principal Contractor undertaking the defects rectification work. This may entail creating a post-occupation risk register and an addendum to the Construction Phase Plan.

### The end of the defects liability period

This should be treated as a new construction project. The Principal Contractor role will remain in place by virtue of the Main Contractor's and Sub-contractors' continuing involvement in the contract. The Principal Designer's appointment will in the majority of projects have ended at the time the Health and Safety File was handed over. Where complex reworking of failed construction is required, it will almost certainly be necessary to appoint a Principal Designer.

### Reactive rectification

In some instances immediate action may be required to undertake repair or reinstatement works. These should, if they occur in isolation, be treated as individual construction projects under CDM 2015, and dealt with according to their size and complexity.

**4**

# STANDARD AND EXEMPLAR DOCUMENTS

## 4.1 Resourcing, fees and appointment

### Proposal for Principal Designer role

It is essential that Designers should be sensibly recompensed for the duties and associated risks they are taking on to adequately perform the Principal Designer role. It is recommended that:

- A Brief for the role of Principal Designer is agreed with the Client. This will be based on the Client Brief (if received). If no written Client Brief is forthcoming, it is recommended that a Client Brief is provided by the Principal Designer recording the briefing discussions with the Client in writing.

- Input required (personnel and required hours) should be assessed once the Brief for the role of Principal Designer has been agreed (and it is recommended that the Principal Designer Brief is agreed before assessing the input required by the Principal Designer). Input required needs to identify who is doing what and when (using the programme agreed within the Client Brief and Principal Designer Brief).

- It is recommended that an Association for Project Safety Form of Appointment for the role of Principal Designer is used.

(http://www.aps.org.uk/publications)

**SAMPLE PROPOSAL FOR PRINCIPAL DESIGNER ROLE**

TO BE USED IN CONJUNCTION WITH APS FORM OF APPOINTMENT

| 1.0 | THE PROJECT | |
|-----|-------------|---|
| 1.1 | The project consists of: | |
| 1.2 | This proposal is based on the following list of provided information: | |
| 1.3 | The contract value is approximately: | |
| 1.4 | The project is to be carried out as a one/two-stage tender: | |
| 1.5 | The intended programme is: Construction commencement: Completion: | |

| 2.0 | APPOINTMENT |
|-----|-------------|
| 2.1 | Our appointment will be in accordance with The Association for Project Safety Form of Appointment as Principal Designer 2015. |
| 2.2 | Collateral Warranties will be provided, in a form acceptable to our PI insurers, to Purchaser, Fund and up to two Tenants. |

| 3.0 | PROFESSIONAL INDEMNITY COVER (PI) |
|-----|-----------------------------------|
| 3.1 | The practice carries PI cover on an each and every claim basis ................................................................................................................................ |
| 3.2 | The maximum liability attached to the practice resulting from this contract will be contract value up to £.......................................................................... |
| 3.3 | Without prejudice............. the liability of [Practice Name] shall be further limited ............ |

*Please remember to discuss disclosure of information regarding PII cover with your Insurer*

| 4.0 | WORKS ELEMENTS |
|------|----------------|
| 4.1 | The scope of our works listed below are in relation to Regulation 11 of the CDM Regulations 2015. |
| 4.2 | The schedule of services we will provide is as listed below: |
| | |
| | |

| 5.0 | CLIENT'S ROLE |
|------|----------------|
| 5.1 | Under CDM 2015 the Client or their Adviser has the following duties: |
| | |
| | |

| 6.0 | ASSUMPTIONS/INFORMATION BY OTHERS |
|------|------------------------------------|
| | |
| | |

| 7.0 | FEES |
|------|------|
| 1. | Our fees for the Principal Designer role will be a lump sum/time and material (delete as appropriate) of £.............. Our fee proposal is also subject to the programme noted within 1.5 above. Should the programme be elongated beyond the dates noted we will advise on any additional fees payable. This fee is exclusive of VAT but inclusive/exclusive (delete as appropriate) of expenses. |
| 2. | The fees are to be paid in .............monthly instalments of £............exc VAT. [add payment terms] |
| 3. | Additional costs if required: |
| | |
| | |

This template can be downloaded from the APS website at
www.aps.org.uk/guidance/principal-designers-handbook

## Programme change letter

This is example text for a letter from the Principal Designer explaining why a change in the programme is necessary in order to deal with health or safety risk management.

Address line 1
Address Line 2
Address line 3
Postcode

Dear XXXXXX

In reviewing the overall construction and design programme(s) for the project we are concerned about the amount of time that has been allowed between preparing the design for [x] and the issuing of tender documentation. There would appear to be insufficient time to adequately prepare the Pre-Construction Information for issuing to potential Principal Contractors who will be tendering to carry out the work. We recommend that the programme is adjusted to enable this to be properly carried out.

We also consider that insufficient time may have been allowed for the Principal Contractor to plan and prepare for construction work, including preparation of the Construction Phase Plan, before you (the Client) allow work to start on site.

In our view it would therefore be appropriate to consider adjusting the start date by a suggested period of [X days/weeks] to [date]. We suggest that, if necessary, this should be discussed and resolved at the next design/project team meeting.

Sign off

This and other sample letters can be downloaed from the APS website at www.aps.org.uk/guidance/principal-designers-handbook

## Late appointment 'with qualifications' letter

The following is sample wording for a letter from the Principal Designer to the Client – this example assumes that a Principal Contractor is already appointed. The letter can be adapted according to the circumstances.

Address line 1
Address Line 2
Address line 3
Postcode

Dear XXXXXX

Appointment as Principal Designer under the Construction (Design and Management) Regulations 2015

Further to your confirmation of our brief for the role of Principal Designer for the above project in your letter/email/fax/verbal instruction of [date], and in view of the lateness of the appointment we note that considerable design, preparation, planning and other Pre-Construction Phase work has already been undertaken and construction work will commence/has commenced on [date]. Accordingly, we need to advise you that the normal role as Principal Designer will have to be modified as follows to achieve effective design and project risk management and compliance from this point forward:

- You must notify the relevant enforcing authority (usually the HSE) immediately and include our details. Submitting this notification demonstrates that you have approved the particulars and that you are now aware of your duties under the CDM Regulations 2015.

- We will review the Pre-Construction Information already provided to those designing and planning the works, and if necessary collect further relevant Pre-Construction Information from you, the Client, and advise you of any further inspections, investigations, surveys or other works necessary to obtain relevant information, residual hazard and risk information about the site or your site activities, and information about the current (if applicable) and future use of the structures as a workplace (if applicable), and pass this on to the Designers.

**[If construction has already commenced]**

As construction work has commenced, we would recommend that you consider putting any further construction work on hold until the Construction Phase Plan has been prepared and found to be suitable, bearing in mind that there is already a risk to you (the Client) of prosecution for the probable breach of your duty under regulation 4(5)(a) of the CDM Regulations.

Sign off

This and other sample letters can be downloaed from the APS website at www.aps.org.uk/guidance/principal-designers-handbook

## 4.2  Pre-Construction Information

Pre-Construction Information is relevant and proportionate Client information (already in the Client's possession or obtainable) and includes information:

- About the project
- For planning and management of the project
- On health and safety hazards, including design and construction hazards and how they will be addressed
- In any existing Health and Safety File

The following sets out the main areas that must be covered in the Pre-Construction Information, and suggests a way to structure this information.

### Description of the project

- Project description
- Key dates
- Project directory – details of other parties
- Extent and location of existing records and plans

### Client's arrangements and requirements

- Timing and sequence of appointments
- Review of designs
- Planning and managing construction
- Communication

- Site security

- Welfare provision

- Environmental restrictions and existing on-site risks

- Significant design and construction hazards

- Health and Safety File

## Environmental restrictions and existing on-site risks

Health hazards

- Asbestos

- Storage of hazardous material

- Contaminated ground

Safety hazards

- Existing services

- Information contained in earlier designs, e.g. pre-stressed concrete planks or post-tensioning

Other

- Boundaries

- Adjacent land uses

## Significant design and construction hazards

- Suggested work methods, sequences, etc.

- Arrangements for coordinating ongoing designs

- Significant risks identified during the design with appropriate information to allow management of these risks

- Materials requiring particular precautions

## 4.3  Design Risk Management

Principal Designers need to understand and bring about the process of Design Risk Management for the construction project.

Designers need to take into account the General Principles of Prevention and any Pre-Construction Information to eliminate, so far as is reasonably practicable, foreseeable health and safety risks to those:

- Carrying out or liable to be affected by construction work

- Maintaining or cleaning a structure

- Using a structure designed as a workplace.

If it is not possible to eliminate these risks, the Designer must, so far as is reasonably practicable:

- Take steps to reduce or, if that is not possible, control the risks through the subsequent design process

- Provide information about those risks to the Principal Designer

- Ensure appropriate information is included in the Health and Safety File.

The Principal Designer must manage the above process (and ensure it happens) for each and everyone of the Designers involved in the project. This is best accomplished by combining the assessed results from Designers into a Design Risk Register.

## Design Risk Register

A Design Risk Register is a live document used to log the risks that have been identified on a project. This makes them easy for the Principal Designer and other duty holders to access them as necessary. Further, it enables the Principal Designer to:

- Manage the process of Design Risk Management by assessing the input from each and all of the Designers (and re-assessing) as the project proceeds

- Identify (with Designers) the need for further Pre-Construction Information from the Client

- Consider the affects of one design solution on other designs (and vice versa)

- Identify necessary information produced with the design for passing to

    - other Designers (as part of the Pre Construction Information)

    - Principal Contractor/Contractors (as part of the Pre Construction Information)

- Identify necessary information produced with the design for inclusion in the Health and Safety File.

| SAMPLE DESIGN RISK REGISTER | |
|---|---|
| DOCUMENT TITLE: | DESIGN RISK REGISTER |
| DOCUMENT FIRST ISSUED: | |
| CLIENT: | |
| DOCUMENT PURPOSE: | |

| Date | By | Details | |
|---|---|---|---|
| | | **TENDER ISSUE:** SOME DESIGN WILL BE THE CONTRACTOR'S RESPONSIBILITY AND THIS DOCUMENT SHOULD BE RE-VIEWED AFTER THE PRINCIPAL CONTRACTOR IS APPOINTED. | |
| For further revisions, insert the date, by whom and ref. no. in the columns below. In the Risk Register, strike out the text to be amended (do not remove) and insert revised text. Adjust the risk colour code as required. Revisions can be reviewed at Design Team meetings. | | | |
| Date | By | Ref. | Details |
| | | | |
| | | | |
| | | | |
| | | | |
| | | | |
| | | | |
| | | | |
| | | | |
| | | | |
| | | | |
| | | | |
| | | | |
| | | | |
| | | | |
| | | | |

**Figure 4.1**
Sample design risk register

## PRE-CONSTRUCTION PHASE DESIGN RISK REGISTER

| PROJECT: | |
|---|---|
| DATE: | |
| VERSION: | |
| LEGEND: | ■ Very likely to happen resulting in fatality or disabling injury<br>■ Unlikely to happen but resulting in fatality; likely to happen resulting in injury or illness; almost certain to happen resulting in first aid injury<br>■ Very unlikely to happen resulting in first aid injury or illness<br><br>Hazard = Something with a potential to cause harm<br>Significant Risk = Risks that are not likely to be obvious to a competent Contractor or other Designer, unusual or likely to be difficult to manage effectively |

| Ref. No. | Ele-ment / Activity | Hazard | Persons at Risk | Risk Level | Risk Owner | Design measures taken to eliminate or reduce hazard | Residual Risk Level | Information provided about the residual hazard | Further Action: Add to PCI Add to Drawings - D Add to H&S File - F | Subcontractor Responsibility Competence check / design responsibility |
|---|---|---|---|---|---|---|---|---|---|---|

### General site issues

|  |  |  |  |  |  |  |  |  |  |  |
|---|---|---|---|---|---|---|---|---|---|---|

### Substructure

|  |  |  |  |  |  |  |  |  |  |  |
|---|---|---|---|---|---|---|---|---|---|---|

### Superstucture

|  |  |  |  |  |  |  |  |  |  |  |
|---|---|---|---|---|---|---|---|---|---|---|

### Services

|  |  |  |  |  |  |  |  |  |  |  |
|---|---|---|---|---|---|---|---|---|---|---|

### Maintenance and Cleaning Operations

|  |  |  |  |  |  |  |  |  |  |  |
|---|---|---|---|---|---|---|---|---|---|---|

Further information and guidance on Design Risk Management can be found on the APS website at www.aps.org.uk/guidance/principal-designers-handbook

## 4.4 Health and Safety File

During the Pre-Construction Phase, the Principal Designer is responsible for the preparation of a proportionate Health and Safety File containing health and safety project information likely to be needed during any subsequent project.

The Health and Safety File is a live document that needs to be appropriately reviewed, updated and revised by the Principal Designer during the Pre-Construction Phase, as the project proceeds.

The Principal Contractor must provide the Principal Designer with relevant information for the Health and Safety File as the project proceeds.

If the Principal Designer's appointment ends before the end of the Construction Phase, the Principal Designer must pass the Health and Safety File to the Principal Contractor. It is generally recommended that the Principal Designer appointment lasts until the end of the Construction Phase to enable:

- Completion of the Health and Safety File by the Principal Designer

- Uninterrupted continuation of the Principal Designer role to cater for Design Risk Management that inevitably occurs during most of the Construction Phase

At the end of the project, the Principal Designer, or where there is no Principal Designer, the Principal Contractor, must pass the Health and Safety File to the Client.

The File must contain information about the current project likely to be needed to ensure health and safety during any subsequent work, such as maintenance, cleaning, refurbishment or demolition.

When preparing the Health and Safety File, information on the following should be considered for inclusion:

- A brief description of the project

- Hazards that have not been eliminated through the design and construction processes, and how they have been addressed

- Key structural principles

- Hazardous materials used

- Information regarding the removal or dismantling of installed plant and equipment

- Health and safety information about equipment provided for cleaning or maintaining the structure

- The nature, location and markings of significant services, including underground cables, gas supply equipment, fire-fighting services, etc

- Information and as-built drawings of the building, its plant and equipment.

## Document control sheet

A Health and Safety File should be prepared for every project involving more than one Contractor, and this should be done proportionately depending on the size and type of project. In some very small projects it may be sufficient for a Health and Safety File to comprise only one or two pages. However, for most projects the following general format can be used.

The File should be properly titled with project (job) reference, version number and issue date.

| [Project Title] | | | |
|---|---|---|---|
| Health and Safety File | | | |
| Reference No | [Reference Number] | Version | [Version] |
| Date | December 2015 | | |

The File will be developed at various stages in the life of a project, with information on significant residual risks added to the working file as design and construction work progresses. It is possible that the File could be issued in an incomplete form for others to complete – for example, if the Principal Designer duty holder changes or terminates and the duty is handed to the Principal Contractor.

| VERSION | PURPOSE OF ISSUE/ AMENDMENT | PREPARED BY | REVIEWED BY | AUTHORISED BY |
|---------|------------------------------|-------------|-------------|---------------|
|         |                              |             |             |               |

It is important to provide information on the various duty holders in the File. This will be important for future construction projects.

| VERSION | DUTY HOLDER | ORGANISATION | CONTACT | FORMAT | DATE OF ISSUE |
|---------|-------------|--------------|---------|--------|---------------|
|         | Client | [Organisation] | [Name] | Digital/ hard copy |  |
|         | Designer 1 | [Organisation] | [Name] |  |  |
|         | Designer 2 | [Organisation] | [Name] |  |  |
|         | Principal Designer | [Organisation] | [Name] |  |  |
|         | Principal Contractor | [Organisation] | [Name] |  |  |

## Health and Safety File – sample structure

The table on Pages 80 and 81 shows the structure of a Health and Safety File prepared to accord with CDM 2015. It may also include an introduction, and various appendices as necessary.

The table also shows the typical sections within the Health and Safety File that could contain useful information to impart to those who will undertake future construction work, including cleaning, maintenance, alterations, refurbishment and demolition, to be carried out safely. Descriptions can be omitted if there is no useful information to be included.

The Client, under the CDM Regulations 2015 has the duty to:

- Ensure that the Health and Safety File is kept available for anyone who needs it to comply with relevant legal requirements

- Pass the Health and Safety File to whoever takes over the structure and takes on the Client duties if the Client decides to dispose of their interest in it

- Ensure that the Health and Safety File is updated with health and safety information following any future work, maintenance or refurbishment that falls within the remit of CDM 2015 involving more than one contractor.

## Information and as-built drawings

As-built drawings for the works should be listed in the File. It is not necessary for the drawing to be incorporated but they can be if appropriate, particularly when the information is provided digitally.

Designers should note that the Regulations require 'as-built' drawings, not the last construction issue, and this means that the Designers and Principal Designer will have to discuss and confirm any deviations from the construction drawings with the Principal Contractor, perhaps recorded only in written Variation Instructions or instructions issued directly to the site.

STANDARD AND EXEMPLAR DOCUMENTS

## Key headings for Health and Safety File

| | DESCRIPTION | REQUIREMENT | APPROPRIATE INFORMATION SUPPLIED |
|---|---|---|---|
| (a) | Description of the works | Brief description of the work carried out | |
| (b) | Residual hazards | Any hazards that have not been eliminated through the design and construction processes, and how they have been addressed (e.g. surveys or other information concerning asbestos or contaminated land) | |
| (c) | Key structural principles | Key structural principles (e.g. bracing, sources of substantial stored energy including pre- or post-tensioned members) and safe working loads for floors and roofs | |
| (d) | Hazardous materials used | Hazardous materials used (e.g. lead paints and special coatings) | |

| | DESCRIPTION | REQUIREMENT | APPROPRIATE INFORMATION SUPPLIED |
|---|---|---|---|
| (e) | Information regarding the removal or dismantling of installed plant and equipment | Information regarding the removal or dismantling of installed plant and equipment (e.g. any special arrangements for lifting such equipment) | |
| (f) | Equipment for cleaning or maintaining the structure | Health and safety information about equipment provided for cleaning or maintaining the structure (e.g. fall protection systems, high reach mobile platforms/ vehicles) | |
| (g) | Location of significant services | The nature, location and markings of significant services, including underground cables, gas supply equipment, fire-fighting services, etc | |
| (h) | Information and as-built drawings | Information and as-built drawings of the building, its plant and equipment (e.g. the means of safe access to and from service voids and fire doors) | |

STANDARD AND EXEMPLAR DOCUMENTS

## Other information

It is often appropriate to provide information in the Health and Safety File relating to specific hazards and risks, particularly where the information has been provided by specialists, not part of the design or construction teams, and these can be included as Appendices:

- Appendix A – as-built drawings

- Appendix B – asbestos survey (complete document)

- Appendix C – other survey information

Other sample formats for the Health and Safety File can be downloaded from the APS website at www.aps.org.uk/guidance/principal-designers-handbook

# KEY CDM ROLES

**5**

Throughout this book, the other duty holders have been referenced as part of the context within which the Principal Designer works. This chapter explains the key roles and responsibilities of all the duty holders under CDM 2015.

## 5.1 Précis of the duties of various duty holders under CDM 2015

This précis provides an outline of the duties and requirements for the various duty holders under CDM 2015. It is, of necessity, an abbreviated version of the requirements of CDM 2015, and needs to be read in conjunction with the Guidance on Regulations (L153), issued by the Health and Safety Executive, to ensure that a full and complete understanding of particular requirements are understood.

The précis cannot, and is not intended to, provide for all the vagaries that occur when undertaking construction work.

For complex situations, it is recommended that definitive advice is sought from an Incorporated, Certified or Fellow Member of The Association for Project Safety to provide full and detailed guidance.

## 5.2  General duties

**Designers and Contactors must:**

- o  be capable of fulfilling their roles (Principal Designers are Designers and Principal Contractors are Contractors)
- o  not accept an appointment unless capable

- Those appointing Designers and Contractors must check the capability of appointees.

- Duty holders must cooperate with any other person working on the project or an adjoining construction site.

- A person working on a project under the control of another must:

  - o  report to that person anything they are aware of in relation to the project which is likely to endanger their own health or safety or that of others

  - o  provide comprehensible information or instruction as soon as practicable.

## 5.3 Client

**The Client must:**

- Make suitable arrangements for managing a project in relation to health and safety including allocation of sufficient time and resources to ensure that:

  - work undertaken, so far as is reasonably practicable, without health and safety risks to persons affected by the project

  - welfare is provided for construction workers

- Ensure arrangements are maintained and reviewed during the project

- Provide Pre-Construction Information as soon as is practicable to every Designer and Contractor appointed, or potential Designers/Contractors

- If there is more than one Contractor on site, at any one time, appoint, as soon as practicable:

  - Principal Designer

  - Principal Contractor

- Failure to appoint the Principal Designer and Principal Contractor results in these roles and associated duties defaulting to the Client (except Domestic Clients - see page 14)

- Ensure that:

  - before the Construction Phase begins, a suitable Construction Phase Plan is in place, prepared by the Contractor or Principal Contractor

  - the Principal Designer prepares a Health and Safety File for the project, that the Health and Safety File is reviewed/revised as necessary and kept available for inspection by those who need it

  - Health and Safety File is passed on when structure is sold/transferred to new Client

The Client must *continued:*

- Ensure that:
  - Principal Designer complies with Principal Designer duties
  - Principal Contractor complies with Principal Contractor duties
- Where there is more than one Client agree, if desired, how certain duties can be undertaken by a single Client entity
- Notify the project, to the appropriate Regulator, and ensure a copy is displayed on site, updating as necessary
- If appointing Designers who are based abroad, ensure that they undertake duties under CDM 2015 for design work undertaken outwith Great Britain for construction work within Great Britain.

## 5.4 Principal Designer (Pre-Construction Phase)

**The Principal Designer must:**

- Plan, manage, monitor and coordinate health and safety matters to ensure that, so far as is reasonably practicable, the project is carried out without risks to health or safety

- Consider the General Principles of Prevention/Construction Phase Plan/ Health and Safety Files when:

  - design, technical and organisational aspects for items of work take place simultaneously or in succession

  - estimating the period of time required to complete such work or work stages

- Identify, eliminate or control, so far as is reasonably practicable, foreseeable risks to the health or safety of any person:

  - carrying out or liable to be affected by construction work

  - maintaining or cleaning a structure

  - using a structure designed as a workplace

- Ensure all Designers comply with their duties

- Ensure, in relation to the Pre-Construction Phase, all persons cooperate with Client, Principal Designer and each other

- Assist the Client in provision of Pre-Construction Information

- Provide Pre-Construction Information, promptly and in a convenient form, to every Designer and Contractor appointed, or being considered for appointment

The Principal Designer must *continued:*

- Liaise with the Principal Contractor and share information relevant to monitoring and coordination of health and safety matters during the Construction Phase

- Prepare a Health and Safety File during the Pre-Construction Phase and review, update and revise as necessary, and:
  - if Principal Designer appointment to the end of the Construction Phase, hand completed Health and Safety File to Client
  - if Principal Designer appointment ceases before the end of the Construction Phase, hand Health and Safety File to Principal Contractor for completion

- Not accept the Principal Designer appointment unless capable

- Provide comprehensible information or instruction as soon as practicable

- Cooperate with others on the site and adjoining sites

- Be satisfied that the Client is aware of their duties under CDM 2015.

KEY CDM ROLES

## 5.5 Designer

**The Designer must:**

- Be satisfied that the Client is aware of their duties under CDM 2015

- When designing, take into account the General Principles of Prevention and Pre-Construction Information to eliminate, so far as is reasonably practicable, foreseeable risks to the health and safety of any person:

  - carrying out or liable to be affected by construction work

  - maintaining or cleaning a structure

  - using a structure designed as a workplace

- If the risks cannot be eliminated, the Designer must, so far as is reasonably practicable:

  - take steps to reduce or control the risks through design

  - provide information about those risks to the Principal Designer

  - ensure appropriate information is included in the Health and Safety File

- Provide sufficient information about the design, construction or maintenance of the structure, to adequately assist the Client, other Designers and Contractors to comply with their duties

- If appointing Designers abroad, ensure they undertake duties under CDM 2015 for designs outside Great Britain for construction work within Great Britain.

## 5.6  Principal Contractor

**The Principal Contractor must:**

- Plan, manage and monitor and coordinate matters relating to health and safety to ensure that, so far as is reasonably practicable, construction work is carried out without risks to health or safety

- Consider the General Principles of Prevention when:

  - design, technical and organisational aspects are being decided in order to plan work taking place simultaneously or in succession

  - estimating the period of time required to complete the work or work stages

- Prepare a suitable Construction Phase Plan before the Construction Phase begins

- Organise cooperation between Contractors

- Coordinate implementation by Contractors of applicable legal requirements for health and safety

- Ensure that employers and, if necessary for the protection of workers, self-employed persons:

  - consistently apply the General Principles of Prevention, and in particular when complying with the provisions of Part 4 (General requirements for all construction sites)

  - where required, follow the Construction Phase Plan

The Principal Contractor must *continued:*

- The Principal Contractor must ensure:
  - suitable site induction is provided
  - prevention of access by unauthorised persons to the site
  - welfare facilities are provided throughout the Construction Phase
- Liaise with Principal Designer and share information relevant to the planning, management, monitoring of the Pre-Construction Phase and coordination of health and safety matters during the Pre-Construction Phase
- Consult and engage with Workers.

## 5.7  Contractors

**Contractors must:**

- Be satisfied that the Client is aware of their duties under CDM 2015

- Plan, manage and monitor construction work carried out either by the Contractor or by Workers under the Contractor's control, to ensure that, so far as is reasonably practicable, it is carried out without risks to health and safety

- Where there is more than one Contractor working on a project, comply with:

  - directions given by the Principal Designer or Principal Contractor

  - relevant parts of the Construction Phase Plan

- If there is only one Contractor working on the project:

  - consider General Principles of Prevention when:

    - design, technical and organisational aspects are being decided in order to plan work taking place simultaneously or in succession

    - estimating the period of time required to complete the work or work stages

  - prepare a suitable Construction Phase Plan before the Construction Phase begins

- Not employ or appoint a person unless they are capable

The Contractor must *continued:*

- Provide each worker under their control with appropriate supervision, instructions and information so that construction work can be carried out, so far as is reasonably practicable, without risks to health and safety, including:
  - suitable site induction is provided
  - emergency procedures
  - information on risks to health and safety
  - other information as necessary
- Not start work:
  - unless prevention of access by unauthorised persons to the site is in place and welfare facilities are provided and maintained.

## 5.8  Workers

Workers are the people who work for or under the control of Contractors on a construction site.

**Workers must:**

- Be consulted about matters that affect their health, safety and welfare

- Take care of their own health and safety and that of others who may be affected by their actions

- Report anything they see which is likely to endanger either their own or others' health and safety

- Cooperate with their employer, fellow workers, Contractors and other duty holders.

KEY CDM ROLES

## 5.9 CDM Adviser

The CDM Adviser is not a statutory role. The CDM Adviser can give advice to the Client about how to discharge Client duties, and advice to Principal Designers, Designers, and Principal Contractors about how to discharge their respective duties.

The CDM Adviser need not be a Designer or Contractor, but should have considerable and in-depth knowledge of construction health and safety. The CDM Adviser to the Client could be the appointed Principal Designer, provided they are a Designer and have sufficient skills, knowledge and experience. The main areas on which they can advise include:

- Preparation of a Client's brief for the project
- Making suitable arrangements for managing the project, including time and other resources
- Making suitable arrangements to ensure that the construction work can be carried out without risks to the health or safety of any person affected by the project
- Welfare facilities provided for the construction work
- Project management arrangements maintained and reviewed throughout the project
- Pre-Construction Information to be provided by the Client
- The Construction Phase Plan drawn up by the Contractor or by the Principal Contractor
- Preparation of the Health and Safety File during the Pre-Construction Phase

- The suitability or otherwise of the Construction Phase Plan and the provision of the proposed welfare facilities prior to construction work commencing on site

- What reasonable steps the Client should take to ensure that:

  - the Principal Designer complies with their duties

  - the Principal Contractor complies with their duties

- Disposing of the building or structure and handing over the Health and Safety File

- Notification to the Health and Safety Executive, or the Office of Rail Regulation, or the Office for Nuclear Regulation instead of the Executive as appropriate.

The CDM Adviser can, if required, advise the Client on the health and safety skills, knowledge, experience and, where it is an organisation, the organisational capability and resources of proposed Designers and/or Contractors prior to arrangements being made for design or construction work to begin.

## CDM Adviser to the Principal Designer (Sub-consultant to the Principal Designer)

In circumstances where the Lead Designer or the other Designers on the project are unwilling or incapable of undertaking the Principal Designer role, but the Client is insistent on the Lead Designer (or one of the other Designers) becoming the Principal Designer, the Lead Designer (or any of the other Designers) can appoint a design organisation with the capability to undertake the CDM 2015 duties as Principal Designer.

The Designer appointing the Sub-consultant retains full responsibility and liability for the Principal Designer service provided by the Sub-consultant.

In most respects the Sub-consultant will virtually undertake the Principal Designer role and will enter into a contract accordingly, with the exception of key interfaces with the other duty holders, such as:

- Distribution of Pre-Construction Information to Designers and Contractors
- Handing over the Health and Safety File to the Client; this should be undertaken by the appointed Principal Designer.

The Sub-consultant will be able to represent the appointed Principal Designer as required at design team and Principal Contractor liaison meetings, and at site progress meetings.

The Sub-consultant will carry appropriate professional indemnity insurance for the delivery of the Sub-consultant's services.

## When the Client becomes Principal Contractor

Clients who control the way in which any construction work is carried out must also comply with (or at least take into account) the requirements of regulations 17–35 (in Part 4 of the Regulations) so far as they relate to matters in the Client's control. This also applies to Domestic Clients (regulation 16 (3)). Those Clients who project-manage a series of Contractors and instruct those Contractors when to carry out work and in what manner, may find themselves unwittingly becoming a Principal Contractor, with the corresponding CDM duties. This can have particular complications and implications for the actions of Designers and Contractors on self-build projects.

# REFERENCE

Training and support

Bibliography and reference material

# Training and support

The Association for Project Safety (APS) believes that their members should possess the right skills, knowledge, qualifications and experience. Capability is also about the willingness to deliver resources for the benefit of project health and safety, the Client's business objectives and for an integrated project team.

The APS provides the industry with Membership Lists of Individuals and Businesses to support Clients and project teams needing to appoint with confidence those that are capable of fulfilling a CDM 2015 role.

As well as providing a platform to network and share good practice, the APS provides access to expert advice, the latest information and support when members need it.

Ongoing membership of the APS and participation in the CPD programme can help members meet their initial and annual accreditation requirements, and support them in their career path to becoming an industry leader in Pre-Construction Health and Safety Design Risk Management.

Whether in the early stages of a career or a qualified and experienced professional, the APS offers advice and routes to accreditation and entry into our professional membership. The APS hosts numerous national CPD seminars across the United Kingdom each year. Through national and regional CPD provision, the APS aims to give our members every opportunity to keep up-to-date with the latest issues in construction health, safety and environmental risk management. The CPD Certification Service provides support, advice and recognised independent CPD accreditation compatible with global CPD principles.

As an APS member you will be kept up-to-date and well informed; you will have access to the Members area of the APS website, our bi-monthly magazine, *Digest*, keeping you informed of important developments and issues in the sector, Practice notes, and regular member eBulletins. In addition to this you will have access to our technical panel and legal advice service, free of charge to APS Members.

# Bibliography and reference material

APS Form of Appointment as Principal Designer:
https://www.aps.org.uk/shop/aps-form-of-appointment-as-adviser-to-principal-designer-2015.html

APS Form of Appointment as CDM Adviser to the Client:
https://www.aps.org.uk/shop/aps-form-of-appointment-as-cdm-adviser-to-client.html

APS CDM 2015 – What Commercial Clients need to do:
https://www.aps.org.uk/guidance/cdm2015

APS CDM 2015 – What Domestic Clients need to do:
https://www.aps.org.uk/guidance/cdm2015

APS CPD presentations CPD35 and CPD36 provided source material and illustrations for this publication

The Construction (Design and Management) Regulations 2015, Health and Saftey Executive, 2015: http://www.hse.gov.uk/construction/cdm/2015/index.htm

Managing health and safety in construction – Contruction (Design and Management) Regulations 2015 – Guidance on Regulations (L153), Health and Safety Executive, 2015: http://www.hse.gov.uk/pubns/priced/l153.pdf

CITB guides:
http://www.citb.co.uk/health-safety-and-other-topics/health-safety/construction-design-and-management-regulations/

RIBA Plan of Work 2013: http://www.ribaplanofwork.com/

Construction Industry Council (CIC) Scope of Services:
http://cic.org.uk/services/the-cic-scope-of-services.php